Happy Birthday, Frog

Frog

Mouse

Lamb

Cow

A play by Joy Cowley
Illustrations by George Baxter

Mouse:
Happy birthday to you,
Happy birthday to you,
Happy birthday, dear Froggy,
Happy birthday to you.

2

Lamb:
Happy birthday to you,
Happy birthday to you,
Happy birthday, dear Froggy,
Happy birthday to you.

3

Cow:

Happy birthday to you,
Happy birthday to you,
Happy birthday, dear Froggy,
Happy birthday to you-oo-oo.

4

5

Frog:
Thank you, Mouse.
Thank you, Lamb.
Thank you, Cow.

Mouse:
You're welcome.

Lamb:
You're welcome.

Cow:
You're welcome.

7

Frog:
Hoppy birthday to me,
Hoppy birthday to me,
Hoppy birthday, dear me-ee,
Hoppy birthday to me.

8